QUICK STArT™ draw, PRINCESSES AND BALLERINAS

Carolyn Scrace

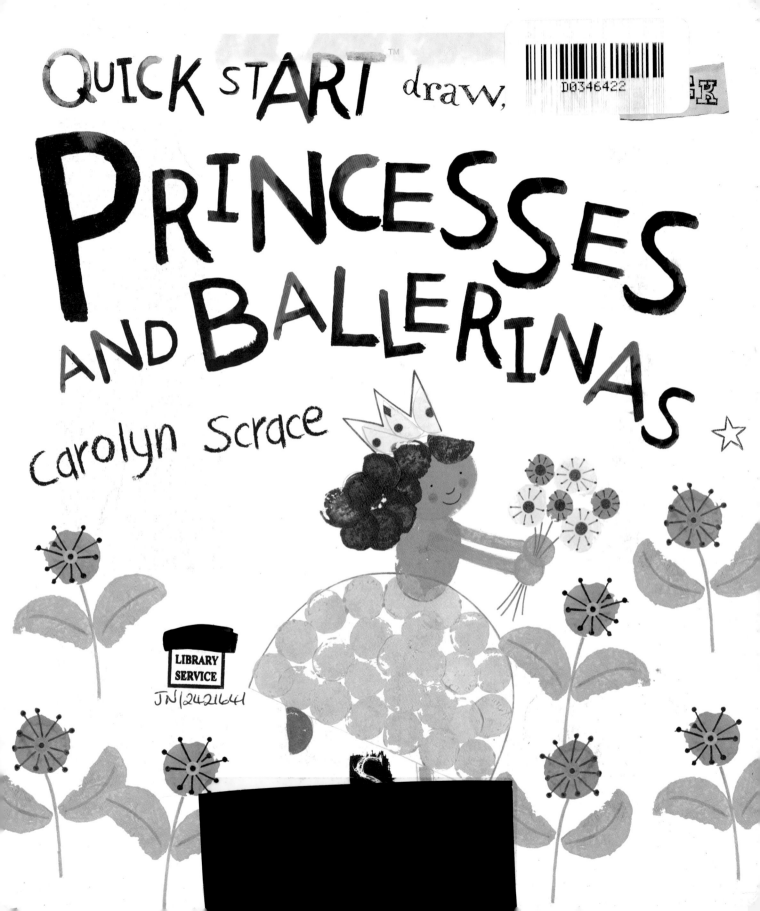

Artist

Carolyn Scrace graduated from Brighton College of Art, England, after studying design and illustration. She has since worked in animation, advertising and children's publishing. She has a special interest in natural history and has written many books on the subject, including *Lion Journal* and *Gorilla Journal* in the *Animal Journal* series.

How to use this book

Follow the easy, numbered instructions. Simple step-by-step stages enable budding young artists to create their own amazing works of art.

What you will need

On each page you will find a list of basic art materials. Some crafts involve the use of scissors, so adult supervision is advised.

Published in Great Britain in MMXVIII by Scribblers, an imprint of
The Salariya Book Company Ltd
25 Marlborough Place,
Brighton BN1 1UB
www.salariya.com

SALARIYA
SCRIBO BOOK HOUSE SCRIBBLERS

© The Salariya Book Company Ltd
MMXVIII

ISBN-13: 978-1-912006-18-2

1 3 5 7 9 8 6 4 2

A CIP catalogue record for this book is available from the British Library.

Printed and bound in Malaysia.

Visit
www.salariya.com
for our online catalogue and **free** fun stuff.

Contents

Crayon Princess

Pencil crayons are ideal for drawing and colouring. Build up rich tones with layers of colours, or create interesting textures by scribbling.

You will need:
- Pencil crayons
- Drawing paper

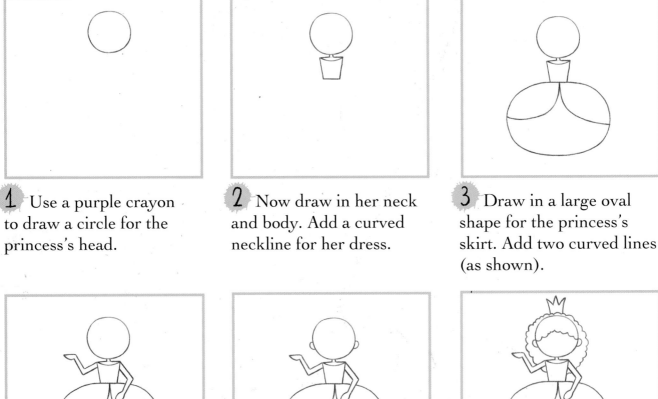

1 Use a purple crayon to draw a circle for the princess's head.

2 Now draw in her neck and body. Add a curved neckline for her dress.

3 Draw in a large oval shape for the princess's skirt. Add two curved lines (as shown).

4 Carefully draw in her arms and hands.

5 Add her feet and draw in her two little ears.

6 Draw in the princess's long curly hair and tiara.

Draw a tiny bird sitting on the princess's hand. Colour it in.

Colour in her face, arms and shoulders with a brown pencil crayon. Make her hair black and the top of her dress pale blue.

Draw in some hills, trees and flowers. Add the sun and clouds, and then colour everything in.

Draw dots on the princess's skirt and colour around them with dark blue.

5

Waxy Ballerina

Use a wax crayon to do your drawing and paint over it with watercolour paints. The paint will resist (run off) the wax line so you can paint over it.

You will need:
- Wax crayons
- Thick cartridge paper
- Watercolour paints

1 Use a red crayon to draw a circle for the ballerina's head.

2 Now draw in her neck and body. Add a 'V' shaped neckline for her tutu.

3 Draw in her pretty tutu. Add her two little ears.

4 Sketch in her legs, knees and feet. Add her ballet shoes.

5 Draw in her arms. Use a black crayon for her face, hair and bow.

6 Use watercolours to paint her face, arms and legs. Paint her tutu pink.

Use pink paint for
her ballet shoes and
hair bow. Add black
paint to finish off
her hair.

Use a yellow crayon to
draw in the stage curtains.
Add white crayoned dots
for the pattern. Now paint
the curtains pink.

Paint the background
yellow.

7

Tissue Paper Princess

You will need:
- Black felt-tip pen
- Thick cartridge paper
- Coloured tissue papers
- PVA glue

Use tissue paper in lots of different colors to make this pretty princess.

1 Use a black felt-tip pen to draw a circle for the princess's head.

2 Now draw in her neck and body. Add a curved neckline for her dress.

3 Add a large skirt and two puffed sleeves for her dress. Now draw her two little ears.

4 Carefully draw in the princess's arms, hands, feet and slippers.

5 Now draw in her hair and crown. Add her eyes, nose and mouth.

6 Tear black, brown, pink and purple tissue paper into small pieces to glue onto your drawing.

Tear out small pieces
of orange tissue paper
to glue onto your
princess's crown.

Add a tissue paper sun and
make branches with leaves.

Tear out pink and blue
tissue paper spots to
glue onto her dress.

Draw a frog
beside your
princess. Glue
on tissue paper
to add colour.

9

Chalk Ballerina

Chalks can be used in many different ways. Try scribbling with the tip, or lay the chalk on its side to make a broad band of colour. Use your fingertip to smudge the chalk to create a soft effect.

You will need:
- Black paper
- White chalk
- Coloured chalks
- Scrap paper to rest your drawing hand on
- Eraser with a point

1 Use white chalk to draw a circle for your ballerina's head.

2 Now draw in her neck and body. Add two tiny ears.

3 Draw in your ballerina's outstretched arms.

4 Draw in the ballerina's long, wide skirt. Add her feet.

5 Now draw in her hair with a big bow. Add the neckline of her tutu.

6 Use the chalks to add colour. Lay a blue chalk on its side to colour in her skirt.

10

7 Use an eraser to draw in her eyes, nose and mouth. Add blue spots to her bow. Draw in the stage and curtains.

Painted Shapes Ballerina

Build up the shape of a ballerina by painting a series of simple shapes.

You will need:
- Poster paints
- Paintbrush
- Cartridge paper
- Felt-tip pens

1 Paint a circle to make the shape of your ballerina's tutu.

2 Now paint in a rectangle shape for the top of her tutu.

3 Paint in a circle for her head with a small square for her neck. Add long rectangles for her arms.

4 Now paint two more long rectangles for her legs. Add her feet and hands.

5 Paint simple shapes for her hair and tiara. Add her rosy cheeks and ears, and paint in her ballet shoes.

6 Use a black felt-tip pen to draw in her eyes, nose and mouth. Finish off her tutu with felt-tip pens and white paint.

Paint a yellow oval of light for your ballerina to dance on. Add a dark blue background, some stars and a moon.

13

Handprint Unicorn

Have fun making a messy handprint, then draw and paint it to turn it into a magical unicorn!

You will need:
- Poster paint
- Large paintbrush
- Small paintbrush
- Coloured paper
- Felt-tip pens
- Scissors
- PVA glue

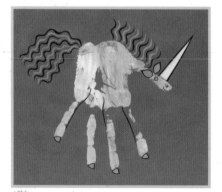

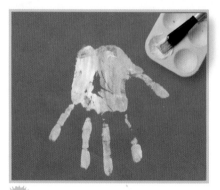

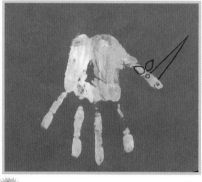

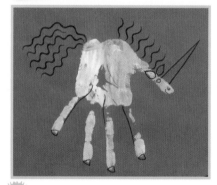

1 Paint your hand with poster paint and press down onto paper. Leave to dry.

2 Use a felt-tip pen to draw the unicorn's ears, eye, nostril and magical horn.

3 Draw in its long wavy mane and tail. Add four tiny hooves and lines on its legs.

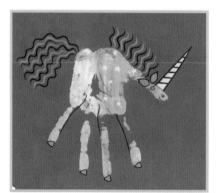

4 Paint in the unicorn's eye, ears, mane and tail. Paint its horn and hooves.

5 Paint magical stars on its body. Use a felt-tip pen to draw lines around its horn (as shown).

6 Carefully cut around your unicorn. Glue onto coloured paper.

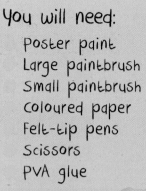

Now try making your handprint into something new – a princess, a castle or even a dragon!

Add some fingerprint flowers and leaves.

Princess

Castle

Dragon

Paper Cup Princesses

Transform a simple paper cup into a lovely princess using just a few simple materials.

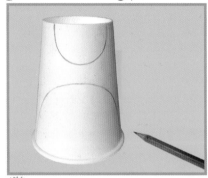

1 Use a pencil to draw in the shape of your princess's face and her skirt.

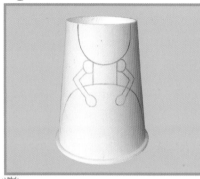

2 Draw her body in between. Pencil in circles for her sleeves and draw her arms and hands.

3 Now draw in her ears, eyes, nose and mouth. Add her long curly hair.

4 Paint in your princess's dress, face, arms, hands and hair. Add spots to her skirt. Paint the rest of the cup pale green.

5 Use a felt-tip pen to draw in her eyes, nose and mouth. Paint her cheeks pink and add pink dots to her dress.

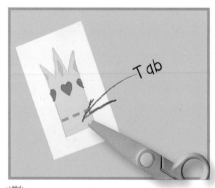

Tab

6 Draw her crown on paper with a tab at the base (as shown). Paint it, leave to dry and cut out. Fold along the dotted line.

7 Cut narrow strips of black paper. Wrap them around a pencil to make curls to glue onto your princess's hair.

Apply glue to the tab, then stick your princess's crown to the flat cup top.

Here are two more princess ideas to try out.

Painted Pebble Ballerinas

Big, flat pebbles are easiest to work on.

You will need:
- Pencil
- Poster paints
- Paintbrushes
- Pebbles
- Cupcake cases (paper)
- Paper
- PVA glue
- Strong plastic bottle cap
- Felt-tip pens
- Scissors

1 Paint the pebble with white poster paint and leave to dry.

2 Pencil in your ballerina's head and body.

3 Then pencil in her arms and hands.

4 Carefully draw in your ballerina's legs and feet.

5 Paint in her head, hands, legs and feet. Paint her top and leggings, and then paint the background a darker blue.

6 Use a felt-tip pen for her eyes, nose and mouth. Paint in her hair and ballet shoes. Add dots and stripes (as shown).

7 To make her tutu, cut out the base of two (or more) paper cupcake cases. Pull each one over her head and arrange in place.

Place the base of your pebble ballerina in a plastic bottle cap so she stands up.

Paint a brown circle on a piece of paper. Leave to dry. Cut it out and glue it on top of her head to finish off her hair. Add a pink paper bow.

Paint the bottle cap to match your pebble colour.

Here are two more painted pebble ballerinas for you to try.

Painted Paper Chain Ballerinas

You will need:
- Long rectangle of paper
- Pencil
- Poster paints
- Paintbrushes
- Scissors
- Fine nibbed felt-tip pens

With this fun project you can create a whole row of dancing ballerinas!

FOLD

1 Fold a rectangle of paper in half (as shown).

2 Fold in half again (as shown).

FOLD

Tutu

Bun

3 Now pencil in your ballerina's head and body.

4 Draw in her tutu so it extends beyond the edges of the paper. Add her legs.

5 Pencil in both arms to extend beyond the edges of the paper, too. Add her bun.

6 Cut around the ballerina shape but take care not to cut the edges where the arms and tutu extend out. (Ask an adult to help.) Open out your paper chain of ballerinas and lay flat.

Pencil in all the ballerinas' heads then draw their tutus, tops, leggings and shoes. Now paint them in any colours you choose.

Finish off the ballerinas' faces and add spots and patterns to their tutus. Use felt-tip pens to draw any fine details.

Printed Princess

Potatoes and carrots make ideal printing blocks. Ask an adult to cut them in half or into shapes (as used here).

You will need:
- Pencil
- Felt-tip pens
- Large paintbrush
- Potatoes and carrots
- Paper
- Poster paints

1 Halve a large potato and draw around it for the shape of your princess's body. Use a smaller potato for her head.

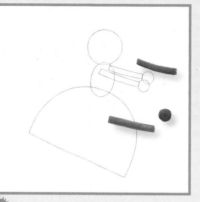

2 Draw around carrot sticks and round slices for the shape of her arms and hands. Draw in her skirt.

3 Cut a carrot slice in half and draw around it for the princess's feet and crown. Draw in her hair.

4 Paint each potato with colour and press down to print her head and body. Print her arms and hands with carrot sticks and slices.

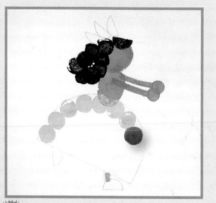

5 Use carrot slices to print coloured shapes for your princess's hair and skirt (as shown).

6 Use a half slice of carrot to print her shoes and crown. Draw in her eyes, nose and mouth with a felt-tip pen.

Use felt-tip pens to draw in her crown shape and add some coloured jewels.

Print trees and flowers from potatoes and carrot sticks. Use felt-tip pens to draw in some detail.

Make a pretty bunch of flowers for your princess. Use slices of carrot to print the flowers and add detail with felt-tip pens.

23

Collage Castle

You will need:
- Pencil
- Thin white paper
- Green paper
- Thin blue card
- Scissors
- PVA glue
- Black felt-tip pen
- Old wrapping paper, corrugated paper, felt, buttons, wool, foil, sequins, leaves etc.

Use a whole variety of different materials to bring your castle to life.

1 Pencil in a curved shape for the hill. Draw the castle tower on top.

2  Draw its pointed roof. Add a window and door to the castle.

3  Draw a princess's head and body at the window. Scribble over the reverse side of your drawing.

4  Turn your drawing, place it onto green paper and use a pencil to transfer the curved hill shape. Glue in place on blue card.

5  Repeat this step using felt for the castle tower and wrapping paper for the roof. Add a corrugated paper door. Glue in place.

6  Cut out shapes for the window and princess. Glue in place. Glue on leaves to make trees, then add paper tree trunks.

Use a felt-tip pen to add the princess's eyes, nose and mouth. Cut long lengths of wool for her hair and glue it on top of her head.

Make your princess's crown out of gold paper. Glue on some sequins and stick down onto her hair.

Cut out some silver foil clouds and glue in place.

Use a felt-tip pen to draw a line down the centre of the door. Glue on two small buttons for handles.

Cut out some flower shapes from wrapping paper and glue in place.

25

Paint and Fold Paper Ballerinas

You will need:
- Rectangular sheet of thick paper
- Coloured paper
- Pencil
- Poster paints
- Paintbrush
- Scissors
- PVA glue
- Fine felt-tip pen (black)

Give your ballerina a colourful concertina tutu!

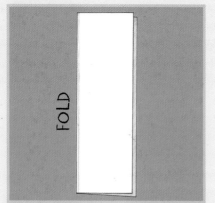

1 Fold a rectangular sheet of thick paper in half (as shown).

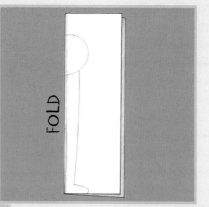

2 Draw half of your ballerina: a semicircle for her head, a line for her body and one leg (as shown).

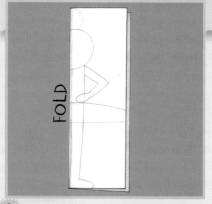

3 Now draw in half of her tutu and pencil in one arm and hand. Add an ear and half of her bun.

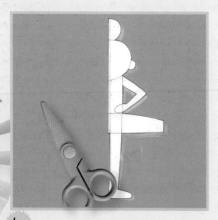

4 Cut around the unfolded edges of your ballerina. Then open out.

5 Draw in her face and hair. Pencil in stripes on her top and leggings. Add her ballet shoes.

6 Paint her head, hands and legs. Then paint her stripy top and leggings and her ballet shoes.

7 Fold a long rectangle of coloured paper into a concertina shape (as shown).

8 Glue one end of the concertina onto the right-hand side of the ballerina's tutu (as above). Bring the other end of the concertina round to the other side and glue it.

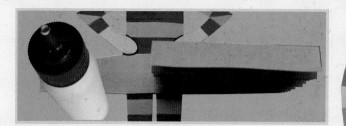

Use a felt-tip pen to draw in your ballerina's eyes, nose and mouth.

Here are two more painted paper ballerinas for you to make.

Torn Paper Ballerina

You will need:
- Pencil
- Thin paper for tracing
- Coloured paper
- PVA glue
- Black felt-tip pen

Make sure you have clean hands when you are tearing your paper.

1 Pencil in simple shapes for the ballerina's head and body.

2 Draw in the shape of her arms, hands and neck. Add the shape of her hair.

3 Draw in her skirt, legs and feet. Add the shape of her hair. Scribble over the back of your drawing.

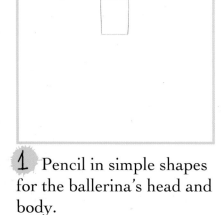

4 Press down hard to transfer each part of the drawing onto different coloured papers.

5 Use the transferred lines to tear out the shapes of her head, hair, arms, legs, feet and tutu.

6 Arrange the shapes in position and glue onto coloured paper.

Tear out a paper bow for her hair, and shapes for her ear and cheeks. Glue in place.

Use a felt-tip pen to draw in your ballerina's eyes, nose and mouth.

Tear out little circles of coloured paper for the pattern on your ballerina's tutu. Glue in place.

Tear out paper shapes for her ballet shoes and glue in place.

29

Mosaic Castle

Build up a picture from small rectangles and triangles of coloured paper glued closely together.

You will need:
- Thick black paper
- Thin white paper
- Pencil
- Yellow pencil crayon
- Coloured papers
- PVA glue
- Scissors

Keep

1 Pencil in the castle keep. Draw in a rounded door.

2 Now draw a tall tower with a pointed roof on either side. Add another tower on top of the keep.

3 Pencil in two little pointed roofs on either side of the door. Draw a line above the door.

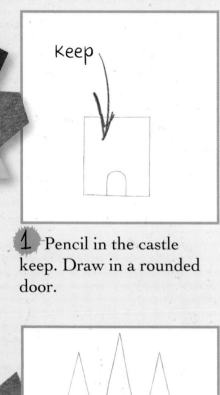

4 Add some windows to your castle. Draw a hill in the background and a path leading to the castle door.

5 Scribble over the back of your drawing with a yellow pencil crayon. Place the drawing on black paper to transfer yellow outlines.

6 Cut strips out of coloured paper, then cut them into squares and triangles. Glue these onto your drawing.

7 Use blue, purple and red mosaics to colour in the keep and turrets. Add a brown mosaic door, a blue path and green hill in the background. Add a mosaic moon and some stars.

Glossary

Ballerina a female ballet dancer.

Collage an artwork made from various materials pasted onto a surface.

Keep a square building, the part of a castle that defenders could retreat to if needed during a battle.

Mosaic an artwork made from small coloured pieces of glass or other materials.

Technique method used to produce an artwork.

Texture the look and feel of the surface of a material or picture.

Turret a tower set at the corner of a castle.

Tutu a dress with a frilly skirt worn by ballerinas.

Wax resist the use of a wax crayon to draw and block out areas from watercolour paint.

Index